Let's Count!

The Count loves to count!

  Count and color **3** bats.

1

2

3

1

The Number 1

1 one

The Count is ready to start counting.

  Count and color **1** castle.

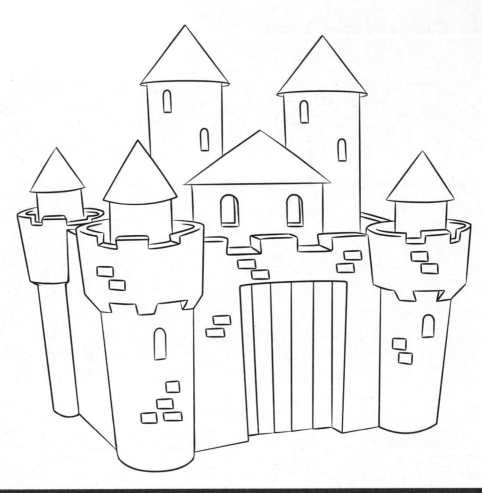

  Trace the number **1**. Then write some of your own.

Count to 1

 Circle each group with **1**.

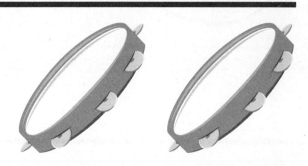

3

The Number 2

2 two

Zoe wears ballet slippers when she dances.

  Count and color **2** ballet slippers.

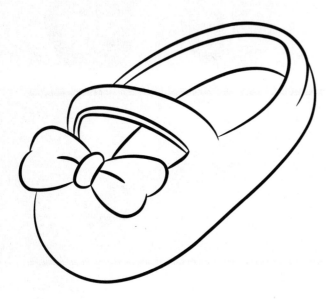 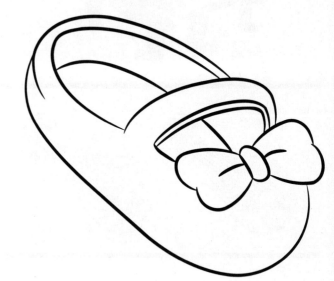

 Trace the number **2**. Then write some of your own.

 4

Count to 2

 Circle each group with **2**.

Explore More

Help your child count the shoes in his or her closet. First count each pair of shoes. Then count each shoe. Have fun counting other things that come in pairs such as socks or mittens.

3 three

Elmo is playing with monster trucks.

  Count and color **3** monster trucks.

  Trace the number **3**. Then write some of your own.

3 3

6

 Circle each group with **3**.

The Number 4

Snuffy is having fun skating.

  Count and color **4** roller skates.

 Trace the number **4**. Then write some of your own.

$4 \quad 4$

  Draw **4** stripes on each rocket.
Then circle **4** rockets.

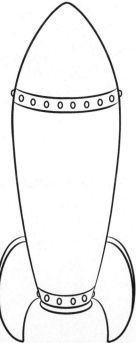

SESAME STREET

5 five

Big Bird is going fishing.

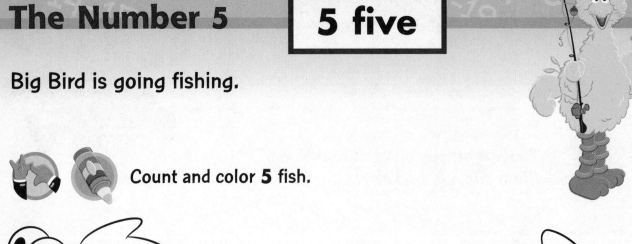

 Count and color **5** fish.

Trace the number **5**. Then write some of your own.

Counting with The Count

Count to 5

 Circle **5** birds.
Then draw more boats to make **5** in all.

Explore More ■ ◆ ● ■ ◆ ● ■ ◆ ● ◆ ●

Give your child a "hand" counting! Have your child practice counting from
I to **5** by counting the fingers on one of your hands. Your child may have
fun counting toes too!

SESAME STREET

Grover in Space

Super Grover thinks counting is out of this world!

  Say the numbers in the picture.
Then color the spaces using the color key.

1=   2=  3=  4= 5=

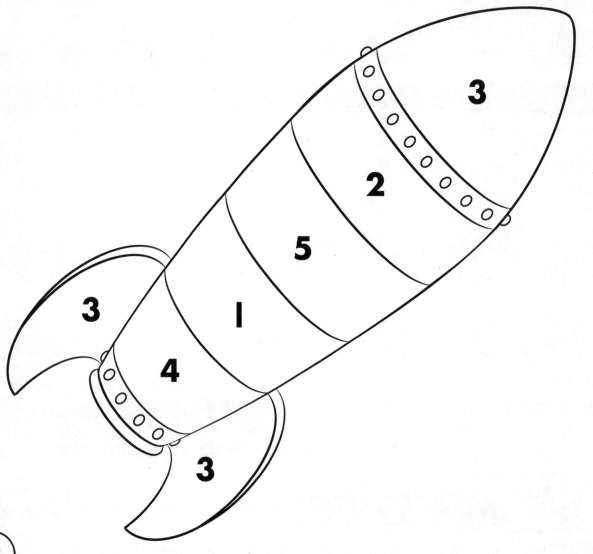

12

Count Your Lucky Stars

 Count the stars in each group.
Then circle the number that comes next.

1  2  3  4

3  4  3  5

2  3  5  4

3  4  5  2

The Number 6

Cookie Monster eats cookies while The Count counts them.

  Count and color **6** cookies.

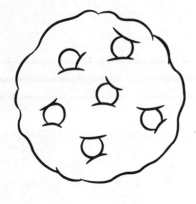 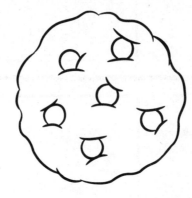 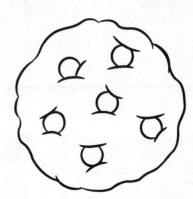

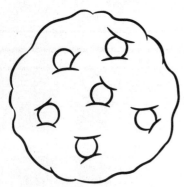 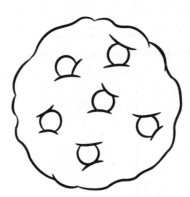 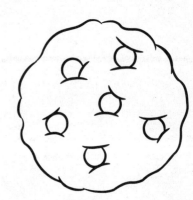

  Trace the number **6**. Then write some of your own.

Count to 6

The Count put candles on the cakes.

  Color **6** cakes.
Then circle the cakes with **6** candles.

SESAME STREET

The Number 7

Ernie loves to take a bath.

  Count and color **7** rubber duckies.

  Trace the number **7**. Then write some of your own.

16

Count to 7

 Draw lines from groups of **7** to the number. Then color the groups of **7.**

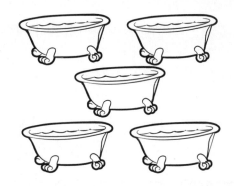

7

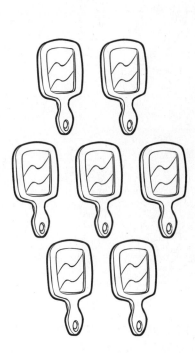

Counting with The Count

SESAME STREET

The Number 8

Bert and Bernice are visiting the pigeons in the park.

  Count and color **8** pigeons.

  Trace the number **8**. Then write some of your own.

8 8

SESAME STREET   Counting with The Count

Count to 8

Circle **8** birds.
Then draw an **X** on **8** birdhouses.

19

The Number 9

Grover is a good waiter. He keeps everyone's water glasses full!

  Count and color **9** glasses.

  Trace the number **9**. Then write some of your own.

20

Color **9** saucers.
Then draw more teacups to make **9** in all.

The Number 10

Baby Natasha likes the sound of rattles.

  Count and color **10** rattles.

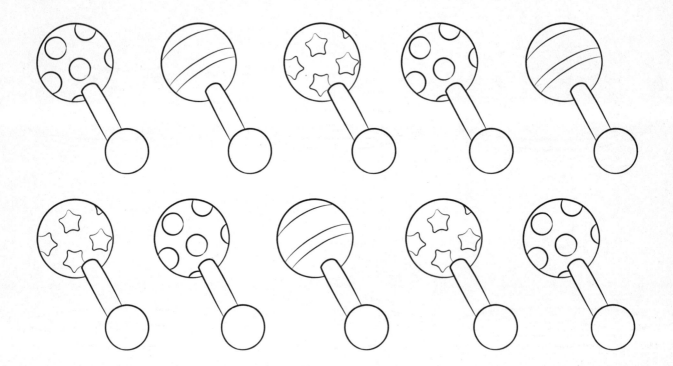

  Trace the number **10**. Then write some of your own.

10 10

Counting with The Count

Count to 10

 Circle each group with **10**.

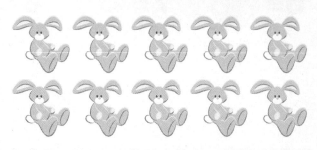

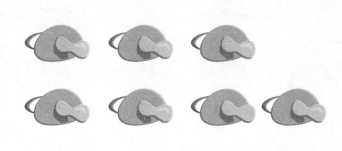

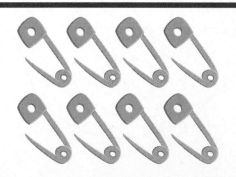

Color by Number

  Say the numbers in the picture.
Then color the spaces using the color key.

6=    **7=**    **8=**    **9=**   **10=**

Count Your Vegetables

  Count and circle to show the number at the beginning of each row.

9

7

10

6

8

The Number 11

11 eleven

Baby Bear is coloring a picture.

  Count and color **11** crayons.

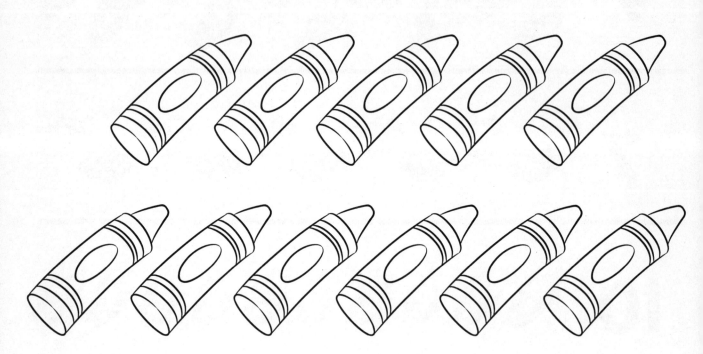

 Trace the number **11**. Then write some of your own.

26

 Count the objects in each group.
Then write the number that shows how many.

_____

- - - - - - - - - -

_____

_____

- - - - - - - - - -

_____

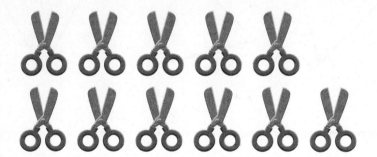

_____

- - - - - - - - - -

_____

Explore More ◆ ● ■ ◆ ● ■ ◆ ● ■ ◆

Play a number guessing game with your child. With your finger, write the
number 11 on your child's back. See if he or she can guess the number.
Then practice with other numbers your child has learned.

Counting with The Count   SESAME STREET

The Number 12

12 twelve

Telly Monster can never have enough triangles.

  Count and color 12 triangles.

  Trace the number 12. Then write some of your own.

12 12

 Counting with The Count

Count to 12

  Count the donuts.
Then draw more to make 12 in all.

Explore More ◆ ■ ● ■ ◆ ● ■ ◆ ● ■

There are dozens of ways to practice counting! Place objects such as buttons, paper clips, or dry cereal in an empty egg carton. Have your child use the objects to count to 12.

29

The Number 13

Bert is proud of his bottle cap collection.

 Count and color 13 bottle caps.

  Trace the number 13. Then write some of your own.

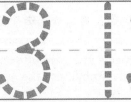

13 13

Count to 13

Draw lines from **13** pennies to the piggy bank.

Explore More

A fun way to practice counting is to use a coin collection or whatever type of collection you may have. Help your child lay out the collection in groups of up to **13** items. Then encourage him or her to count the items in each group.

Counting with The Count

SESAME STREET

The Number 14

14 fourteen

Ernie and The Count can always count on their friends.

  Count and color **14** Twiddle Bugs.

  Trace the number **14**. Then write some of your own.

14 14

Count to 14

 Circle the group with **14**.

 Draw **14** spots on the bug.

Counting with The Count

SESAME STREET

The Number 15

15 fifteen

Oscar loves old stinky socks.

  Count and color 15 stinky socks.

    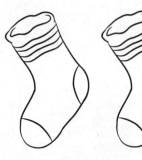

  Trace the number 15. Then write some of your own.

15 15

Count to 15

 Circle each group with **15**.

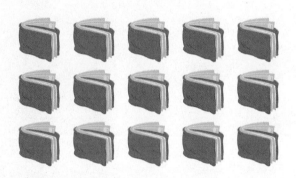

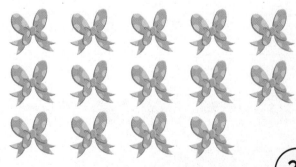

Counting with The Count

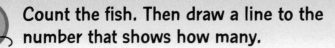

Gone Fishing

Count the fish. Then draw a line to the number that shows how many.

12

15

8

5

11

Musical Monster

 Draw lines to connect the dots from 1 to 15.
Then color the instrument.

37

The Number 16

16 sixteen

Prairie Dawn is watering flowers in the garden.

 Count and color **16** flowers.

 Trace the number **16**. Then write some of your own.

16   16

Count to 16

Count and draw an **X** on **16** pumpkins.

Explore More

Make a sweet **16** collage with your child using old magazines and newspapers. Help your child cut out pictures that show **16** of his or her favorite things. Talk about each thing and then glue the pictures onto a sheet of paper to make a collage.

Counting with The Count

SESAME STREET

The Number 17

The Amazing Mumford has made lots of rabbits appear.

  Count and color **17** rabbits.

  Trace the number **17**. Then write some of your own.

Counting with The Count

Count to 17

  Count and circle **17** favorite pets.

The Number 18

18 eighteen

Elmo is shopping for a new bowl for his friend Dorothy.

 Count and color **18** bowls.

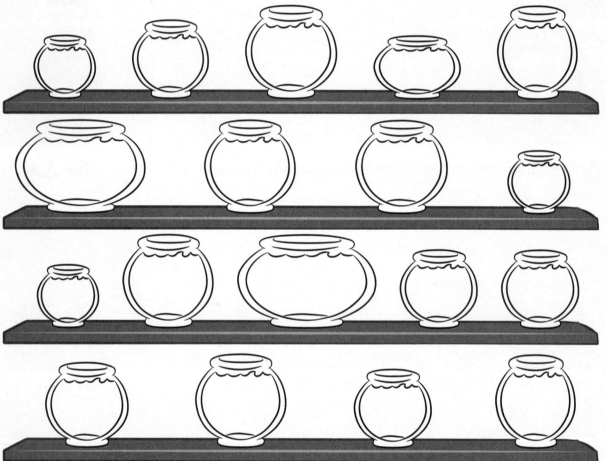

  Trace the number **18**. Then write some of your own.

Count to 18

Count the fish.
Then draw more to make 18 in all.

18

Counting with The Count

The Number 19

19 nineteen

Zoe has lots of hats to try on.

 Count and color **19** hats.

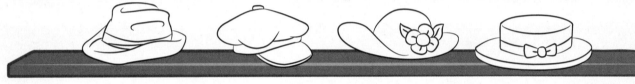

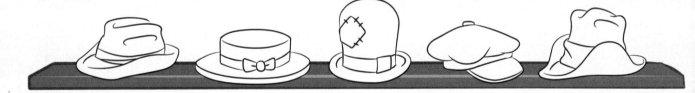

 Trace the number **19**. Then write some of your own.

19   19

19

Count and color **19** circles.

Explore More ▪ ◆ ● ▪ ◆ ● ▪ ◆ ● ▪ ◆ ●

Magnetic numbers are a great way to reinforce number recognition. Put a set on your refrigerator door or on a cookie sheet. Say the numbers and have your child point to and repeat each number. You can also choose three numbers and have your child arrange them in numerical order.

45

Big Bird is finding plenty of pretty seashells.

  Count and color **20** shells.

  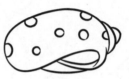 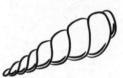

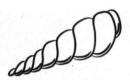    

 Trace the number **20**. Then write some of your own.

20 20

  Count and write the number
of dog bones in each group.

_____

_____

_____

_____

_____

_____

SESAME STREET

Keep on Counting!

  Count from **1** to **20**.
Write the missing numbers.

1   2   4

6   8   10

  12   14   15

16   18   20

Explore More ■ ◆ ● ■ ◆ ● ■ ◆ ● ■ ◆ ● ■

The next time you and your child go for a walk, sing this fun counting song as you count the steps you take.

1, 2, 3, (pause) 4, 5, 6, (pause)
Count your steps as you go.
7, 8, 9, (pause) 10, 11, 12, (pause)
Try it fast or try it slow.

13, 14, (pause) 15, 16, (pause)
Clap along if you choose.
17, 18, (pause) 19, 20, (pause)
It's fun to step and count with you!

48